BELVOIR CASTLE   Photo: Christine Matthews

Message from Emma, Duchess of Rutland,

Patron of Dayglo Books Ltd.

I am delighted to be the Patron of Dayglo Books Ltd. As a person with dyslexia myself, I appreciate these books being available. The people at Dayglo Books have a real passion for making reading more accessible than ever before to dyslexic people. They have foresight and talent and truly believe in the joy of reading for pleasure.

Impact

and other
creative writing

Rebecca Constable

Published by

Dayglo Books Ltd, Nottingham, UK

www.dayglobooks.co.uk

ISBN 978-1-911425-64-9

© Rebecca Constable 2017

Cover artwork by Rebecca Constable
realised by www.valentineart.co.uk

Typeset in Opendyslexic
by Abelardo Gonzales (2013)

Printed in England

Distributed by Filament Publishing Ltd, Croydon

I ask my parents to forgive me for not dedicating this book to them, however I do have an excellent excuse. My loving, ~~slightly crazy~~ extremely crazy godparents. To Auntie Sandra and Uncle Keith, thank you for annoying my brains out about passing GCSE English and making my first book real.

Love you – Beckyboo ☺

Table of Contents

All the art work between the pieces of creative writing are by Rebecca Constable

Author's Note

I chose to write the story 'Impact' as I want to highlight what people dealing with dyslexia may feel like.

Even today, not enough teachers, students, parents, children or members of the public recognise what dyslexia is and how it can impact on your life.

This writing is made up of true experiences. Some are my own and others are my classmates'.

Throughout this story I have not described the main character's appearance. I do not tell you their gender.

Most of the characters do not have names.

This is because appearance, gender or name will not help you get to know the character. On the contrary, it may distract you from the topic of dyslexia.

There are many different ways dyslexia can impact on someone. Therefore, I have introduced several characters with dyslexia, with very different personalities.

There are no distinguishing features to the main character. I am not trying to represent one person but rather the many children, teenagers and adults struggling with dyslexia.

There is no age limit to people with dyslexia so we do not get to see the character's age – maybe 5, maybe 15, maybe 50.

I am very proud that this story won the overall "Nottingham Young Creative Awards 2016."

Rebecca Constable

Message from the Publisher

It is my very great pleasure and privilege to present Rebecca Constable's work to you.

She is a remarkable young woman. To win the City of Nottingham's award "Young Creative of the Year 2016" is a very considerable distinction.

The head of the judging panel made it clear that Rebecca's dyslexia was not taken into account.

Her work was judged purely on its creative merits, as indeed it should have been.

Dayglo Books Ltd has a particular interest in the achievements of dyslexic people of all ages. So I certainly do take Rebecca's dyslexia into account. She communicates vividly the pain and distress that dyslexia caused her.

Even today, in some places, there is still a lingering stigma attached to dyslexia. It is brave of Rebecca to speak frankly about feelings of low self-esteem and fear of ridicule.

It is hugely to Rebecca's credit that she has overcome these things.

She has challenged the world not to think any the less of her because she is dyslexic. And she shines a bright light on what is often a hidden, private misery.

Rebecca is "young and creative". Here at Dayglo Books we have some not-so-young and creative people. We the believe innovative presentation of this book is a world first.

This book is being offered on a choice of six different tints of paper. A dyslexic reader can select the one that works best for them. We hope this will provide an easy and pleasurable reading experience.

With all the other subtle adaptations built into the text, we want our dyslexic readers to enjoy Rebecca's book in every aspect.

As the author says, "All it takes is one voice to give others inspiration and confidence."

Let it be Rebecca's voice, indeed!

Gloria Morgan

Managing Director

THE**I**R

That is their toy!

W**I**TCH

It's the wicked witch's hat!

L**OO**K

Look at them over there!

bed

~~Empact~~

~~Impacked~~

~~Impaked~~

IMPACT

~~I am confident~~

I have no confidence

~~I can do this~~
I will fail

~~I work hard~~
I am lazy

Words blacker than night drilling into my head, consuming me, overpowering me, describing me.

I am a failure. I am dumb.

I will never get this right.

~~I am special~~
I have a disability

~~I have dyslexia~~
I am stupid

~~I am not alone~~
I am alone

I'm sitting in a hard plastic chair. Four walls, two windows and one door. Twenty-four students surrounding me, one teacher and twenty-five books.

1

Nothing but the occasional scrape of chairs and the flicker of pages; but not mine. My book lies open in front of me, at page 15, chapter 2.

~~I'm doing well~~
I am behind

"I reached that page on my first day," they snigger; ~~the strangers~~ my friends.

My eyes tingle with the threat of tears and words smear together like rain drops on a window. A lump appears in my throat.

Everyone will see.

I let my hair fall like a curtain around my face. I sink into the chair like it's quicksand. I am invisible.

"It is pathetic to cry over a book," they say. ~~The students~~ The teachers.

I am pathetic.

I glue my eyes to the clock, praying for the minutes to tick faster. But they ignore my wishes, mocking me as they move lazily by.

A tear escapes from the corner of my eye. It sprints down my cheek. I beg my body to turn translucent – to become nothing but air particles – to evaporate like the last drops of water trapped in the desert.

But it doesn't work.

"BILLIE!"

I jump. Pain shoots up my legs as they collide with the hard wooden table. Laughter is ringing in my ears.

Miss Reid the ~~malicious monster~~ teacher approaches.

I lift my head ever so slightly.

I shake a sliver of hair from my face. All eyes are on me. Red paint drips from my cheeks as she towers over me. She is waving a piece of paper like a flag in a parade.

"**Two hours** you sat there and you only answered **two questions!** This is not good enough!"

She slams the papers down. My head is swelling like a balloon. The papers reveal half-answered questions in untidy writing.

My untidy writing, my wrong answers.

I stuff my face into my hair, shoving the test out of sight. A low rumble disturbs the silence as they laugh.

My blood is replaced by fire. My heart is pumping nothing but pure adrenaline. I want to run. I want to storm out of this prison and never come back.

But I can't. I won't draw more attention to myself.

I bite my lip so hard I taste blood. My eyes marry the clock. I begin to wish the minutes away all over again.

. . . . . .

Ice, like words, is both dangerous and beautiful. However, unlike words, I only see the beauty in it.

I am free – free to skate and glide and jump. The students aren't strangers but friends. The coaches help us learn. They give us physical examples, not written ones.

Out here, I don't mind the stares. I don't want to evaporate. I can fit in and I can stand out. I decide.

I know what I am doing. One toe loop, three crossovers, five back spins, one spiral and two twizzles.

Routines and dances that force my body to balance.

I shift my weight and bend my limbs until every muscle aches. The pain is oddly comforting. It means I'm doing this right, I am pushing myself and I'm succeeding.

~~I don't know left from right~~

I look down at my hands – one black glove and one white one. No left or right, just black and white. It's laughable how simple the solution is.

. . . . . .

I'm ~~hiding~~ sitting at the back of the class.

I'm merging with the same plastic chair. I'm staring at the same four walls, two windows and one door.

And I'm watching the same white plastic clock tick the time idly by.

My hands shake as I try to take the spelling test in front of me. I force myself to take deep breaths but it feels like iced water in my lungs. My blood is nothing but ice, showing no signs of melting.

I am frozen in time; trapped in this moment with no escape. Toxic words echo at the back of my head, rotting my brain.

"You only answered **two** questions in **two** hours. **Two questions!**"

"I bet you couldn't even get **those** two questions right."

"Why are you so stupid?"

"Why don't you just pay attention?"

Tiredness fogs my brain as the words start to merge. They are like carriages on a train, locking onto one another. Concentrate.

~~Different, bifferent, b d b bifforant, diffaront~~

I can feel Miss Reid's eyes boring into my back as she stares over my shoulder.

Clipboard in hand, her pen scars the paper with crosses.

Tears burn my eyes once more, sliding down the back of my throat. I carry on to the next word.

. . . . . .

My hands construct a perfectly accurate outline on the paper. Two eyes, two eyebrows and two ears, one nose, one mouth – and several dark hairs trapped in a messy knot at the nape of her neck.

Roses blossom on her cheeks. Fire outlines her blood red lips. The ocean is held in her deep blue eyes. Her sun-kissed skin is creasing around her twinkling eyes and faint dimples pull on her cheeks. She is perfect – confident, beautiful and friendly.

~~Everything I'm not~~

This is my escape. Sketching, painting and printing. Colour, texture and pattern.

No need to think or concentrate. Just draw, imagine and feel.

Fine art, creative art, photography, textiles, graphics.

~~The best subjects~~

The easy subjects.

. . . . . .

Which . . . witch . . . which . . .

One has a T and one without, simple. But which 'which' does the T belong to?

How do you remember to replace it with the H? And then move the T along one letter? Which 'which' is the right which?

I sit in a yellow room four hours every week. The square windows are tinted with twilight. A round wooden desk is stationed in front of me.

Two cards both say 'which', both spell 'which', both sound like 'which'; but both have different meanings, different spellings. So which 'which' is the right which?

"A 'witch', as in a wicked witch, is spelt like this."

He touches the card to his right. David. Not Sir, or Mr, but David.

He's a teacher, my teacher. But he doesn't shout or get frustrated. He's kind and understanding. He compares my work to my previous work, not to other people's work.

I look at the card hidden slightly by his fingertips – witch, the one with the T.

Before I try to explain yet again that it's not that easy to remember, he slides the paper towards him. Then he fishes a pen from his trouser pocket.

"This is how I remember them." He tilts his head to the side, looking for a new angle. He bends his arm awkwardly around the paper, trying not to block my view.

I watch him draw a smooth line from either side of the T.

Then he joins them up at the top to form a soft spike.

And it clicks.

"The top of the T is a witch's hat, which a wicked witch would wear."

I stare at the paper, grinning like an idiot.

I've seen this drawing before but never understood it. Never actually saw it being drawn out in front of me – just the finished result.

The T in 'witch' is a hat,
a wicked witch's hat.

The 'O's' in 'look' are eyes. You
look at something with your eyes.

 The 'i' in 'their' is
a person. It's their toy.

Countless teachers have shown me these
drawings. Some were more patient than others, but in
the end they all gave up.

But David didn't.

He took his time and explained with pictures.
He drew each line in front of me.

Just a simple drawing. Just a simple idea
and a patient teacher.

. . . . . .

"Where were you last night?"

The teacher's late. I'm sitting in this rectangular
prison, in my usual seat, at my usual desk, with my
usual ~~strangers~~ friends, and the teacher is late.

There is nothing else to focus on, and no one to stop the questions.

"What?"

"Where were you?"

"Err, at home."

Her eyes light up and her lips twist into a slow smile.

"I saw you running back into school."

My heart skips a beat. A cotton ball is wedged in my throat.

"I – I don't know w-what – "

"You're going to them extra classes for thick people."

Laughter erupts, bouncing off the four walls. It bounces out of the door and down the corridors and echoes around the school. Rose petals fall from my cheeks and rain stains my eyes. A hundred years pass before the teacher marches into the room, demanding attention.

. . . . . .

It's the last lesson of the day, and the last day of the week.

We are separated into groups and ready for battle. The task is to create a poster featuring tools. The best poster. My mind is swimming with ideas.

We could make the title from tools, making the words become the art. But no one is listening.

~~They never do~~

They give me one job. Draw the hammer.

"Where do you want me to draw it?"

They all look at me as if I've suddenly grown two heads. A short, harsh laugh cuts through me. I spin around, and want nothing more than to die. Miss Reid is standing there, hands on hips, and her shoulders shaking like someone is holding a Taser to them.

"Well done! That may just be one of the most stupid questions I've ever heard."

The whole class is listening, some in fits of laughter, not bothering to hide it.

"Where do you think you draw it? ~~It's not a question~~ ON THE PAPER."

She marches off, stealing the last bit of confidence I own. Laughter fills the room, but mine does not join it.

. . . . . .

The darkness outside seems to soak up the glow of my lamp. Rain slams into my bedroom window in heavy sheets, threatening to smash the glass. I lie in bed trying to shut out the roar of wind and cackles of thunder.

I suffocate myself deep within the warmth of my pillows.

I attempt to drift into a dreamless sleep, but it doesn't work; it never does. Toxic words wrap around my brain like a snake, slowly tightening, suffocating me, until I can ignore them no longer.

"It's pathetic to cry over a book."

"You only answered two questions in two hours."

"Why are you so stupid?"

13

"You're going to classes for thick people."

"I am pathetic."

"That may be **one of the most stupid questions** I've ever heard."

"Why don't you listen?"

"I am pathetic."

Laughter fills the room, because I am pathetic.

A hurricane of emotion bubbles up inside me: anger, hurt, embarrassment. They swirl and mingle like a tornado with nowhere to go.

I don't listen.

I am stupid.

I am dumb.

Every breath feels like fire in my lungs.

I don't want it anymore. I don't want the air; the food that grows on this diseased planet; the water that hides the earth's wounds.

This world is poison. The atmosphere is broken and the people are toxic . . .

I don't want to be part of it anymore.

. . . . . .

My legs shake as they try to support me. My teeth slam together so hard I feel it vibrate through my bones. My heart pumps nothing but fiery adrenaline – but yet I feel ice cold.

It's test day.

Head down, back hunched, arms shielding my chest, I slip into the classroom like a ghost.

I glide to my usual seat at the back of the room. But my name is not there. Instead, there on the desk is Claire Thomson's name printed in bold lettering. My eyes scan the hall. On each individual desk lies a name tag. I shuffle to the fifth row, but my name is not there.

Fourth? Nope.

Third? My heart is in my mouth.

Second? My blood is replaced with fire.

First?

My brain stops working. It refuses to read my name printed out in the same bold writing.

I risk a glance around the room. Everyone is taking their seats. They make sad faces when they are separated from their friends and cheer when they are not.

My head spins. I collapse into the hard plastic chair. The desks are shaking; the chairs are shaking; the floor is shaking.

The whole world is shaking – crumbling – falling.

Breathe!

Heels click behind me. A clock ticks and papers shuffle. The teacher calls for order and the test starts.

My heartbeat is the only sound in the school, the only sound in the world.

But is it?

A faint murmur drifts through the room
– a whisper caught in the air currents, unable to break free.

"Why does he get help?"

"Yeah!"

"What makes him so special?"

"That's unfair."

"He's cheating!"

I cringe as the uproar begins. A boy I don't recognise sits across from me with an elderly woman at his side. She is reading the text, piecing this foreign language together and making it recognisable.

"Why don't we get help?"

"Yeah – help us!"

"Why is he the favourite?"

The class goes into a wild madness which not even Miss Reid can control.

Their voices clash together like claps of thunder. The teachers storm around the room like rhinos on a rampage.

Finally, one voice can be heard over the chaos. One harsh, stressed voice, which silences these animals and sends a chill shattering down my spine. Four words.

"BECAUSE HE CAN'T READ!"

My heart forgets to pump. My lungs forget to take in oxygen. For a spilt second, there's not a breath in the air. Everyone is a perfect statue, nothing but a photograph.

"Damn, Miss! I like to make an introduction, but most people start with my name!"

A flash of silence and then laughter.

Shoulder-shaking, stomach-aching laughter.

For one split second I'm ashamed to find my own laughter mingling with the others. But then I see the new boy's shoulders are shaking just as much as mine and I relax. We are laughing **with** him, not **at** him.

. . . . . .

18

When he said 'I like to make an introduction' he wasn't kidding.

"THAT'S IT, GO AND SIT ON THE NAUGHTY TOOLS!"

He roars like a madman, flapping his arms in the air like a bird trying to take off.

A fit of uncontrollable giggles erupts from behind me.

"Clearly you have no respect for the art of drama," he laughs. "I was in the zone."

"Well maybe you should get out of the zone and pay attention to the script. It's stool, not tools."

"What!" He presses the script to his nose, examining it. "Aw, man, someone moved the S again!"

Laughter follows his words like a rat looking for food.

That's Charlie; the new boy. Confident, funny, loved and dyslexic. I wonder how he does it, how he's so relaxed about **everything** and how he can joke about **anything**.

He's never embarrassed, or shy. He reads out loud, he laughs at mistakes. He's friends with everyone. People laugh with him, respect him, accept him.

I want that, I **will** have that; because this time I have hope. I have living, breathing proof that things can be different, because I ~~can~~ will make them different.

I will be confident, relaxed, respected, dyslexic and successful.

.   .   .   .   .   .

"I lie there unmoved, my body weight crushing the soft snowflakes hidden under me.

I don't know how long I've been here. A day? A month? A year? Probably longer. Time doesn't seem to exist here. It's like nothing is moving forward. It's like I'm frozen here, in this exact moment.

But time must be passing, right? I'm older, bigger, stronger – no, not stronger.

I think I was nine when it took me, clawed me right from my bed like I was some sort of prize in

a grabber machine. Stole my life right from under me
and trapped me in this hell.

They want my locket it said – the shadow – it
holds some sort of power I don't fully understand."

I grip the book tighter, heart racing, blood
pumping. It's so descriptive, so emotional, like
a movie playing in my head.

But instead of watching the characters on
a screen, I become the character.

I am sucked into this fantasy world. I feel their
fear and love. I laugh at their jokes and cry at their
losses.

This is my escape from reality – something no
one can destroy.

The pages will not turn fast enough. My brain
won't focus long enough. I am pushing myself more
than any teacher ever did. And I don't even realise it.

I am slowly learning this foreign language. It is
becoming familiar – almost recognisable.

~~I always lose what line I'm on~~
My fingers keep me on the right track

~~The words are too hard for me~~
I let some words swim over my head

~~The description is too much for me~~
I let myself get lost in the description

~~Reading is torture~~
Reading is leisure

. . . . . .

I am sitting in the centre of the ~~prison~~ class-room, books and papers spread out across my desk, laughing so hard my ribs hurt.

~~The strangers~~ My friends are surrounding me doubled over laughing ~~at me~~ with me.

I wonder when I stopped caring – stopped fighting them, stopped hating them.

When I stopped being the depressed victim and started being one of them.

I told them how I felt. I told them that I was dyslexic and learned I was not alone. There are six people in this room who felt the same as I did, and sometimes still do.

But instead of tearing each other down – laughing out of relief that someone else made the mistake or got caught having extra classes – we help each other, correct each other and learn from each other.

All it took was one voice to stand out from the crowd. To speak the truth for others. To say 'stop lying to yourself'.

One voice to give others inspiration and confidence. One voice – my voice – to change my future.

~~I have no confidence~~
I am more confident

~~I can't do this~~
I will do this

~~I am lazy~~
I need help

~~I have a disability~~
I think differently

~~I am stupid~~
I have dyslexia

~~I am alone~~
I am not alone

. . . . . .

Disbelief fills my frozen body.

I hear my mum scream before I reach the end of the page, but I still don't believe it. I am dreaming, hallucinating.

My brain will not function. It won't read the sheet balanced in my numb hands. My blood is replaced with water, then fire, then ice.

I don't understand.

My head is spinning, my mum is screaming and I don't understand.

Graphics	B
Art	Distinction
Science	Distinction
Maths	C
Resistant materials	B
English	A
Performing arts	Distinction

I passed?

My heart pumps faster. My blood is replaced with adrenalin.

"I passed."

I hear my voice saying the words, but they feel unfamiliar in my mouth.

"I PASSED!" My head stops spinning, but I don't understand what I'm saying. I look around the room full of students collecting their exam results, celebrating or crying – I can't tell. My brain won't distinguish between tears of joy or sadness.

A

English A

A English

Pass

I half expect someone to rip the paper out my hands and shout 'April Fool!' But no one does.

I look for someone to take the paper back, saying someone made a mistake. That these aren't my results. But there it is, my name printed in bold clear writing at the top of the page.

My name

My results

My success

My A

Congratulations! Your place to study at Nottingham Trent University has been confirmed.

We look forward to meeting you on the 25th of September 2015.

Read on for more Short Stories!!!

A Shadow

in the Night

A shadow moves silently through the abandoned night. It leaves no corner untouched and lurks in the dark alleyways and street ends. Snow falls on footprints which are not there. A ghostly hand creeps up a vine-covered wall.

It unlocks a child's window, forcing the icy air to explode into the fiery room.

The dark figure slithers up to the sleeping child, who shivers in the snowy breeze.

A locket is fastened around the girl's neck; a locket which should never be taken!

. . . . . .

Darkness presses into the silent night like a weightless veil.

Fresh footprints crunch into the icy snow. Rusty keys clank together. Tired feet clamber up rickety stairs.

Dim lights flicker on, and a pearl-pink door creaks open. Screams and warm tears fill the frosty night.

A child is taken.

Shadows flee, people scream, and stars glisten in the dark.

Days, months, years go by. A child grows.
A mother dies. Shadows grow stronger, humans grow weaker. A child is lost forever!

. . . . . .

Ice is thin and weak, scratched and scarred, full of darkness, but yet light.

Lost hopes and dreams lie in the frozen cracks. Darkness hides upon every ridge, every scratch. Death swirls in the still waters below and a locket falls to the snow.

I lie there unmoved, my body weight crushing the soft snowflakes hidden under me.

I don't know how long I've been here. A day? A month? A year? Probably longer.

Time doesn't seem to exist here. It's as if nothing is moving forward. It's as if I am frozen here, in this exact moment, forever.

But time must be passing, right? I'm older, bigger, stronger – no, not stronger.

I think I was nine when it took me. It clawed me from my bed as if I was some sort of prize in a grabber machine. They said they wanted my locket – the shadows. It holds some sort of power I don't fully understand.

. . . . . .

Ice forms on my exposed skin. A bony fingertip brushes under my eye, whipping the frozen tears from my pale cheeks. My lips quiver, but no sound fills the eerie night.

Wings beat in the distance. They fight against the razor wind. My heart flutters in my chest. A sliver of hope glistens in my eyes. I know who's coming – it must be.

I can almost see his face in the darkness – strong and powerful like a god ready for war. I've seen the soft side of him, heard his laughter, as smooth and light as silk.

He helped once, freed me. He took me to his village. He promised it was safe, that not one drop of inky darkness could corrupt it; and I believed him. But he was wrong. We were wrong. They attacked and it was war.

There were screams and sirens and bodies. I'll never forget the bodies – clawing and kicking like animals; mangled with mud and blood.

A slightly wild glow blazed in their eyes, while they fought for their lives – my life.

This is my fault.

. . . . . .

He's closer now. I can hear the racing beats of his heart. I can see the puffs of his breath as they rise and swirl up into the black night. But darkness wraps around us like a blanket. We need help; he needs help.

My hands scramble across the rough ice, desperately searching for my locket, before it's too late.

Shadows move closer, ice lies thinner, cracks grow deeper. A locket clenched in a girl's hand. A locket that should be in use, but remains dormant.

. . . . . .

It's hard to fight something when you can't see or hear it, but somehow he manages to.

He's by my side in seconds. I can feel his icy breath on my bony cheek; see the anger in his watery eyes. I feel warmer, stronger as he cages me in his arms. I listen to the thump of his warm heartbeat that I dreamt so many times had stopped. But it hasn't. It's here – with me – like music in my ears.

A shadow shifts in the corner of my eye. My body turns stiff and cold with panic. We're surrounded, like meat in a shark tank – no not him, he will survive. Darkness pulls closer and my brain fogs with fear, so much fear; for me, for him.

No, concentrate!

I take a shaky breath and close my watery eyes. I'm alone once more!

. . . . . .

A heart races. Fear grows. Shadows fade. A locket glows. Ice melts. Waters rise. A girl is saved by a watchful eye.

The Father Before the Soldier

Royal Navy	35,430
Army	101,300
Royal Air Force	40,090
Total Regular Forces	176,810

We're maths, numbers on a page, a problem, a solution, an answer.

Volunteer Reserves	37,600
Sea Cadets	133,000
Army Cadets	75,800
Air Training Corps	43,000

We're puppets, toy soldiers, broken and fixed.

We're silent shadows, deadly ghosts, dolls with guns.

We take orders, no questios. We fight. We die. We survive. We recover. We live.

U.K. population – 64.1 million. And growing.

We fight for these people, for better lives, for the myth they call peace. We fight for the women, the children, the elderly and the future.

But I fight . . . I fight for my daughter, her life, her peace, her future. I just hope I'm in it.

It's been half a year since I saw her – my daughter. That's 6 months, that's 26 weeks, that's 182 days. That's too long.

. . . . . .

Mother's full name	Emma Thomson
Father's full name	Eric Thomson
Sex	Female

We spent the New Year in the hospital, welcoming a new year and a new life, a new future.

Date of birth	01/01/1991
Time	2:52am
Weight	3.7kg

I was one of the lucky ones.

I remember the day perfectly, I was there, alive, safe, and grateful. I remember the rain pounding the windows, the distant claps of thunder, and the dim flashes of lightning. Emma crushing my hand.

We didn't know then – the gender. We wanted a surprise – correction: Emma did. I secretly hoped for a boy. I imagined taking him down to the fields, playing football, climbing trees, camping, fishing.

But then I saw her, Josephine – our Jo. She was balled up in blankets, heart beating, eyes closed.

And the future I imagined died away. Only to be replaced by a better one, a real one.

. . . . . .

Around 453 sons, daughters, husbands, wives, soldiers, are killed each year. Fighting other people's battles. Killing for a better future.

That's 453 broken families; 453 fresh graves; 453 figures from the maths equation.

453 men and women made murderers – including me.

Some are broken, beyond the repair of prosthetics. Some have an untreatable injury, an invisible injury . . . a fake injury.

I am saved, gifted, protected. I have something to live for, something to fight for, and something to die for.

At 7 years old I took her on her first camping trip. I thought she wouldn't be able to handle the mud, the bugs, the cold, but I was wrong.

At 11 years old I walked her up to the front gates of big school. I expected fear and nerves, but she marched through those gates with determination lodged in her eyes.

At 14 years old I fell victim to witnessing a sleepover. Six girls and me. Enough said about that.

At 16 years old I took her shopping for her first prom dress. For three hours I sat in a waiting room holding dresses heavier than me. But the way her eyes lit up when we found that perfect one . . . I wouldn't have missed that for the world.

At 18 years old I was introduced to the boyfriend.

At 22 years old I became the father of a bride. I walked her down the aisle, heart beating, music playing, and handed her over to the man she loves.

At 25 years old I became a grandfather.

. . . . . .

Dear Daddy

IT'S A GIRL! Your granddaughter was born at 2:35pm on Monday 4th July 2015, weighing 3.9kg. She's strong. She kept us up for three nights straight. She's going to be a fighter, just like her grandfather.

She has our eyes, dark brown, with jet-black hair. I've told her all about you – how you can be strong and determined and stubborn, yet gentle and kind and loving.

I wish you could be here to see her, to hold her, but I understand why you can't, and so will she, one day.

I hope you're staying safe and looking after yourself. We're all here hoping and praying that you'll be with us soon.

I know that you will always be here for us, even if it's not always in physical form. And I'm always there for you. You've given me the best life possible and I can't wait to see you later this year.

Take care of yourself.

Lots of love from your little girl and your new granddaughter.

Jo and Mia

Life in the Pits

The dark

I've never seen such darkness

The cold

I've never felt so cold

Alone

I've never been so alone

Fear

I've never felt such fear

I'm sitting

Waiting

In an endless mask of dust and darkness

I can hear sounds in the distance

Exhaustion

Pain

But mainly fear

Fear of being trapped here

Hundreds of feet down

Fear of never seeing the light;

Sunlight

Oh, how I miss the sunlight

The Gift

Magic is expression, freedom, beauty – or at least, it was . . .

Magic is woven into this village; this world. It was useful, helpful, balance, some would say. Most believe it is a gift from the moon itself, pure and whole. 'Children of the moon' they would call us.

But I don't believe there is anything completely pure and whole in this world. And now I know I was right – right to fear it, right to fight it. Magic is sacrifice, corruption, death . . .

I, like so many others, was born with what they call 'the gift'. Magic.

I was the only one to see it for what it really was; a curse.

Uncontrollable power. Overwhelming duty, to protect, to serve, to keep the peace. And the overbearing stench of death that haunted every corner I turned. I hid it out of fear, told no one, and swore to take my secret to the grave.

The mortals – humans – began to fear us and despise us.

They grew tired of being the weaker race. But they had one advantage, one tiny detail so many of my kind overlooked. They had numbers. They had soldiers, knights, warriors, so many more than us. But we had magic. That was enough. It was supposed to be enough. But it wasn't.

They came for us at first light. This was our weakest moment when the sunlight floods over the moon's power. We were slaughtered, drowned and hung. We were burned at the stake. It was a massacre, a bloodbath. We didn't stand a chance.

There were two brothers, Edward and Kole. I'd seen them before. They both possessed 'the gift', and both were fighting for their lives, their families, and their race. And both were failing.

I watched from the shadows as Edward choked on the end of a rope. He fought until his last breath left him and his body hung limp in the smoke-stained air. I watched his family grieve. His brother was driven into madness. Consumed with anger, he swore to avenge his brother's death.

As his power built and his strength grew, his soul twisted as black as night itself. He was like nothing I had ever seen before. Without a trace of humanity left, he attacked. Thousands fell; hundreds surrendered; few survived.

Black magic oozed through his veins as thick as ink. It boiled his blood as he slashed through to the other side. To Avalon – the land of the dead. A place of light and peace. A place of darkness and terror. A place which is unwelcome to the living and a place that should remain untouched.

He destroyed both worlds in his quest to bring his brother back. Destroyed warlocks, mortals, dead and alive. No one was safe. I knew he had to be stopped, no matter what the cost.

It was time to use my magic, my gift. I rounded up as many as I could, but nowhere near as many as I needed. We trained, and fought, and died. We trusted, we betrayed, we died. We failed.

The night it was over; the night we threw the last of our strength into the battle; the night my family and friends perished; that was the night I felt the true extent of my power for the first time.

That night I became a murderer.

It was like a drug to me; the moon's power-like trance that I could not escape. I felt I was floating in mid-air.

The battle going on around me suddenly felt like miles away. The explosions and screams dulled to a heartbeat. The heat of fire and sweat lifted like smoke. My vision iced over.

Every breath sent agony through my body as it begged for mercy, until my heart refused to beat. A voice vibrated through me, powerful like the Gods themselves: "Keep the peace".

It echoed through my skull. It ripped through my bones. It pumped though my blood, warming my body.

I drag myself back to the battle I had briefly escaped. Suddenly, I see a dagger. Its blade is as silver as the moon itself and as tough as diamonds.

I reach out to grasp it. It clings to my hand as if it were a part of me. It feels alive. That feeling pulses through my veins. It sets them on fire and it drags me towards the man who must die at my hands – Kole.

His powers are useless against me now. His face is thick with blood and scarred with grief. I plunge the dagger deep into his heart. I control his life. My hands are soaked with blood darker than the deepest depths of hell.

He lies on the floor, writhing and twisting. A sickening sun grins down on him, while I steal the air from his lungs.

I have restored the peace and avenged so many who had lost their lives. Kole is dead. Victory is ours.

Invisible Scars

Everything's silent. Everything's still

Not a movement of water or footprint on the
hill

Not a tweet of a bird, not a single word

Not a blink of an eye, not a scream as they die

A ray of sunlight fills the smoky night

Hovering over the lost fight

The ground is bound with blood

And scars lay in the mud

Trumpets sound from far away

Soldiers march to where they lay

Everything's silent. Everything's dead

As everyone bows their head

Not a movement of water or footprint on the
hill

Not a tweet of a bird, but a cry can be heard

It rips through the night as the fire is alight

Everything's ancient. Everything's old

And the earth is lost in mould;

But everything's silent. Everything still

Not a movement of water or footstep on the hill

Not a tweet of a bird, not a single word

Not a blink of an eye, not a star in the sky

Abandoned and lost;

And destroyed for what cost?

We remember red for the fight

And the ghosts that still haunt the night

The ground may be covered with heather

But the scars will lay forever

A Short
Memory

This is possibly the shortest
short story you will ever read.

I stand there, unmoved, as he reaches for me.

Silence falls all around us. A shiver runs down my spine as his icy fingertips trace the deep bloody cut on my arm.

.... Now it's your turn to get creative – finish the story and provide the title illustration!

Altered

Can you open your eyes?

No.

Do you know what colour is?

No.

What do you see?

Emptiness.

I can feel the wind wrapping itself around my body, whipping my hair, squeezing my heart. My heart is on fire, pumping too fast, stopping my breath.

You must see something?

No.

Do you see shadows?

No.

Blackness then, you must see blackness?

What is blackness?

The wind beats harder, faster, stronger, pulling me, pulling into the unknown.

It's been 6 weeks.

The wind is joined by something. Something

solid and cold – snow? It's wet and cold on my skin, and I pull my jacket tighter.

It's been 6 weeks since the operation.

I can hear the waves crash and thump and pound against the rocks from somewhere below. I'm high up. My head spins, my heart pounds. I'm on a cliff. A cliff's edge. Near the sea. Alone.

Can you draw?

No.

My heart pumps nothing but adrenaline.
I feel both free and terrified.

There's snow on the ground. I can feel it. It's soft, yet frozen, crunching under my feet. There's a bench? Yes, a bench to my right. It's wooden and old. I can feel the cracks and the mould, but I sit anyway.

Are you afraid of the dark?

What is the dark?

I've been told I can only see the darkness. Whatever darkness is.

Darkness is black and black is not a colour.

Colour? Red, blue, green, yellow, purple. They are just words to me; useless, meaningless words.

Are you scared?

Am I?

No.

Yes.

Are you hoping it works?

Am I?

Yes.

I don't know.

It's been 6 weeks since the operation.

The bench creeks and groans under the force of the wind. I pray it holds out. I need to do this here. I need to do this now. Alone.

Where are you going?

Out.

Alone?

Yes.

But you – you can't!

Why? Because I'm blind?

Because it's not safe!

Is it safe for anyone?

People see me as broken. Maybe I am. They want to fix me. Maybe I should let them. They think I'm missing out. I might be. They think I need my sight to live a full life. Maybe I do. They wanted to operate and I let them.

How would you feel if I told you there's a chance you can get your sight back?

How do I feel about that?

I don't know.

Everything will change.

Do I want it to?

I will see the world differently.

Do I want that?

Will it make me weaker?

I don't know.

Will I change?

Maybe.

Do I want to change?

The wind is wearing itself out, but the snow is still coming. The sea is still crashing. My heart is still pumping. I breathe. In, out, in, out. The air is crisp, clean, wet. It tastes like salt. It smells like seaweed.

I've had the operation. It's been six weeks.

There's no going back.

Are you excited?

Am I?

Are you scared?

Definitely.

Are you scared it won't work?

I don't know.

Breathe. In, out, in, out. Slow, deep breaths. In, out. My hands shake. I can't do this.

I can't do this. What if it changes everything? What if it has worked? In, out, in, out.

What if it hasn't?

73

It's too late. It's too late to change my mind.
I need to do this, and I need to do this now.

I reach for the dressing taped across my eyes.
My hands shake, my heart pounds, my blood boils.

Breathe. In . . . hold . . . out.

My hands shake and I rip the dressing off.

Nightmare in the Jungle

Screams slowly fade into the icy night as
I race for shelter among the twisted trees and murky
swamps. Blades of dead grass brush against my bare
legs; reeds sway silently in the cool breeze. My feet
sink into the moist earth, and a river trickles softly in
the distance.

. . . . . .

I close my eyes. I struggle to catch my breath
as panic takes over my body. My hands tremble in
fear. Who are they? Where am I? What's happening?

Tears roll down my cheeks as I search for an
escape, but there's nothing; nothing but darkness.
I close my eyes and count back from ten, trying to
calm myself. I wait till my breaths are more even and
my eyes are dry. I take one last deep breath and let
my anger take over.

"LET . . . ME . . . OUT!" I force through my teeth
as the chains holding me prisoner shatter onto the
wooden floor!

. . . . . .

My eyes snap open and I'm flashed out of the
dream. My breaths are short and uneven. But it's not
a dream. It's a memory.

Sunlight burns through the gaps in the leafy trees. Raindrops splatter on my pale cheeks. There's rustling in the bushes behind me. I see a figure move across the lake! I spring to my feet when I realise it's human.

They are here. Here to take me back to that place. I CAN'T go back there!

I bolt down the river bank. I hurdle over thick tree trunks and duck under low branches. My feet beat against the rocky ground before it gives way. Rocks crumble down the hill. I am thrown with them, like a rag doll.

Sharp stones cut into my exposed skin as I come to a halt. I'm in a field. I'm buried in dirt and surrounded by crippled grass.

I scramble to my feet. I am eager to put as much distance between me and them as possible. But I freeze, unable to move, when I realise I'm not alone. I turn my head slightly to the right and I see her, lying in the grass.

A huge lioness is snarling at me, with her cubs hidden behind her. Her eyes meet mine.

She slowly stands, ready to pounce if necessary. But I'm not the one who is threatened.

Rustles emerge from the awakened forest behind me. A shadow slips into the corner of my eye.

I feel my bones lock into place as the lioness's teeth are exposed. Her razor-sharp claws dig into the dried earth, like a newly sharpened knife slicing through butter.

I gasp for air as the shadow creeps closer.

His voice is calm and relaxed as he chants to the lioness, calming her and her cubs. The sound is fluent and high pitched. It's a language I have never come across before, yet I understand every word.

The lioness lies back in place, with her cubs sleeping behind her.

I turn to face the figure waiting behind me. My eyes widen as I take in his long pointed ears placed on the top of his bald, pale head.

His jet-black eyelashes sweep along his snow-white cheek bones. His pointed, rabbit-like nose twitches, exposing two perfectly white rabbit teeth.

He towers above me. He stands with his feet shoulder width apart. He holds both hands above his head, assuring me he is not a threat.

There is something about him that looks familiar. It's as if I know him. I've seen him before. But where? How?

I press my lips tightly together whilst I study his clothes. He wears a well-fitted black leather jacket, a pair of designer dark denim jeans and a plain blue polo shirt.

"I mean you no harm," he whispers, careful not to scare me. When I don't reply, he moves closer. He raises his voice, using a firmer tone when he pleads.

"Please, I mean you no harm, but I really do need your help!"

Bait

"Emily?"

Another step, and then another. She could see a curtain of brown hair wrapping around a pale face, and water around lime-coloured eyes.

It's her! It's Emily.

Another step. Emily's faint whispers were carried in the wind. Lily still couldn't make out what she was saying.

Another step. She was almost there now. Another. She could see blood streaming down Emily's jaw, dripping to her neck. She's hurt.

Lily lunged forward. Emily screamed and this time Lily heard her words.

But it was too late. Something hard slammed into the side of Lily's head. The warm wetness of blood oozed over her skin.

Emily's cries echoed in the back of her head as stars danced across her vision.

"NO! IT'S A TRAP! GET OUT, LILY!"

A Hidden World

My heart races, as the engine roars to life. It shakes and vibrates and rocks as it spits out the water behind us.

I can't believe this is happening!

The wind is slamming into my face. It's damp and cool and mixed with salt. It pulls and twists and knots my hair, but I don't care.

I can't hear anything over the roar of the wind, the crash of waves and the vibrations of the engine as it pulls us forward, throwing us into the unknown.

I try to peel my eyes open against the wind. I want to look forward. I want to know where we are going. I manage to get only a snapshot of blueness before the wind defeats me, but it's enough to set my blood on fire. Blue, everything is blue, nothing but blue.

The boat rocks. I feel someone's body slam into mine. My hand flies out and grabs the first thing I can reach. I pull myself back into my seat.

The boat rocks again. This time I make a mental note not to let go of the metal pole behind me.

Water sprays up into my face and I turn away, angling my body against the wind. I open my eyes just in time to see the last of civilisation disappear behind the horizon.

It's both exciting and terrifying. I'm free yet I'm trapped.

The engine spits out more water behind us. I can't stop my eyes wandering below me.

The water is blue, deep blue, glistening like crystals in the sun. I've never seen anything as pure and untouched by men.

I want to jump in it and swim and swim, down to its sandy bed.

I want to know how deep it goes, I want to explore every coral, every mystery. But then I image what would happen if I did get down there. If I did explore every coral, unlock every mystery.

What would be left? Nothing. Some things are better left untouched.

The change is only slight but I can feel it. the boat is slowing, stopping. My heart is racing. We must be almost there!

The roar of the engine simmers to just a murmur, and we rock gently in the waves.

"Look over there!"

I follow the direction of the pointing finger. I see it. It's beautiful, and gentle. Somehow, I had imagined it bigger.

"Everyone ready?"

I tighten my snorkel, check my flippers, take a deep breath and . . . jump.

For a split second, I tense my body imagining the water to be ice cold but it's not. It's warm and clear and unlike anything I've ever seen before; unlike anything I thought could still exist in this world.

I look down and for a moment I forget why I am here. There is nothing below us, yet I am floating on top of a whole world that is hidden to us. The sunbeams slicing through the water's surface fade into nothing, but deep blue.

'Look!'

My head snaps up, and for a moment
I forget to breathe.

I can't breathe. My breath has left me.
A cotton ball is wedged in my throat.

I see it. It is huge, swimming straight towards
me, mouth open, swallowing half the ocean as it
swims. My heart stops.

It comes closer, gliding towards me, with
a mouth bigger than my entire body. Then it turns,
gliding away again, swimming into the unknown.

I follow it, swimming at its side. The sunlight
scatters and shimmers and shines like broken glass,
as it breaks through the surface. It dances and twists
and sits across this giant's back.

We swim, and swim and swim. I can see small
fish, like silver coins hiding, swimming, feeding from
this giant's back.

Its skin looks like the night sky, a blanket of
deep blue velvet spattered with white crystals.

I swim and swim, but its silky colours are fading. I swim, but its body is shrinking. I swim and swim but the water is distorting its outline, twisting its fins, blurring its skin, fading its colours.

Just like that, it's gone!

Gone, deep below, swimming, sinking back into the ocean.

I let myself float back. Back to a world of noise, and air and smell. A world with gravity and heaviness and weights.

I watch through the cracked, blurred surface until the last of the whale-shark's shadow enters a new world.

I hope have you enjoyed this book full of
extremely short stories ☺

Rebecca Constable

Postscript on 'perceptual distortions'

Many people find that reading gives them a headache because the text is unstable: letters appear to move or to change shape and colour.

These perceptual distortions of text depend on the size and spacing of the letters, and the gap between the lines of text.

The distortions also depend on the colour of the page on which the words are printed.

There is often a particular colour, different for each individual, which can reduce the distortions.

I am delighted that a publisher has responded to the needs of readers for whom conventional text appears unstable in this way.

The instability can interfere with reading, and may be one of many difficulties that can contribute to dyslexia.

Dayglo books are printed in 'OpenDyslexic', a font designed by an individual with dyslexia. The letters and words have more space around them than is conventional, which helps improve clarity.

The books are printed on several shades of paper so that readers can choose the colour that is clearest for them.

It is entirely appropriate that the novel by Rebecca Constable, herself dyslexic, is printed in such a way as to minimise some of the effects of

perceptual distortion.

Prof. Arnold Wilkins

Director of Visual Perception Unit

Department of Psychology

University of Essex

January 2017

This book is presently available with the following 6 choices of tinted backgrounds for the main story "Impact".

You can order any of these tinted backgrounds by using the appropriate ISBN. We call it 'tint on demand'.

The saturation level of these tints is 'Very Light'.

Tint	Name	Example	ISBN to order
Cream	Champagne		978-1-911425-59-5
Grey	Pearl		978-1-911425-64-9
Yellow	Primrose		978-1-911425-63-2
Pink	Quartz		978-1-911425-61-8
Green	Apple		978-1-911425-60-1
Blue	Sky		978-1-911425-62-5

The tints have been arrived at after discussion with Prof. Arnold Wilkins whose generous assistance is warmly acknowledged. This choice of 'tint on demand' backgrounds is exclusive to Dayglo Books Ltd.

Any quantity of any tint, including single copies, can be suppliedby quoting the appropriate ISBN.

The chart below shows the next range of tints in which this title will be produced.

The saturation level of the tints shown below is 'Light'.

Tint	Name	Example	ISBN to follow
Cream	Banana		
Grey	Pebble		
Yellow	Pineapple		
Pink	Cherry Blossom		
Green	Jade		
Blue	Hyacinth		

Over time, more tints in deeper levels of saturation will be added to the range.

This choice of 'tint on demand' backgrounds is exclusive to Dayglo Books Ltd.